Mickey and Minnie are best friends.

"Oh, Donald, you're so strong!"

"Yoo-hoo, Minnie!"

Mickey Mouse Word Find

```
M  I  N  N  I  D  O  N  A
A  P  D  O  N  A  L  D  N
G  L  T  D  L  S  E  G  O
O  G  D  N  Q  I  P  F  D
O  V  O  A  N  Y  F  Y  P
T  D  Y  N  I  O  T  E  L
Q  O  I  P  G  S  Y  K  U
M  M  T  K  W  F  Y  C  T
G  I  C  U  O  T  D  I  O
D  I  N  O  L  G  Z  M  Y
M  Q  G  C  D  P  L  U  T
P  Z  D  A  I  Y  O  F  G
```

MICKEY

MINNIE

PLUTO

GOOFY

DONALD

DAISY

"Gosh! What a swell picnic!"

Best pals!

Goofy studies! (Mickey snoozes.)

START

FINISH

Draw your favorite Disney character.

"Who-o-o-a!"

Which Minnie is different?

Your Answer:

Answer: C

"Aw, shucks!"

"Aw, gee, Minnie..."

Girls' day out!

Rollerblade date!

"There's nothin' to it, Daisy."

Double dip for Donald.

"A-hyuck, A-hyuck! This sure is fun!"

"Gawrsh! A shooting star!"

"Isn't this wonderful, Mickey?"

Daisy is the apple of Donald's eye.

"That smarts!"

"Tea, anyone?"

See anything?

Which piece completes the picture?

A   B   C   D

Your Answer:

Which one doesn't belong?

A

B

C

Your Answer:

Which Mickey is different?

Your Answer:

Minnie has a pretty garden.

"Mickey, aren't you sweet!"

Minnie stirs the soup.

Mickey tosses the salad.

"Mmm…perfect!"

"Flapjacks coming up!"

"Oh, Minnie, I simply love to shop!"

Two for tea.

"Let me down!"

"Let's investigate that fire."

A big bear hug!

Minnie meets a toucan.

How many butterflies do you count?

Your Answer:

"Well, hello, panda!"

This antelope wants to elope.

Square Off!

Take turns drawing a line between 2 dots to make a square.
When you make a square, put your initials in it, and take another turn.
Count 1 point for plain squares, 2 points for squares with Goofy's picture,
and 5 points for squares with Mickey's picture.
When all the dots are connected, the player with the most points wins.

Player 1_____   Player 2 _____

Score _____   Score _____

"What a handsome fan!"

Mickey meets a monkey.

"Whooo are you?"

"Oh, how lovely!"

"I just love stripes!"

Mickey's new beach buddy.

Donald has a whale of a good time!

Donald's nephews find some frog friends.

"Thanks a lot!"

"What a sweet elephant calf."

"My hat!"

Word Find

```
D R W U N S V D S
B A N E D R A G Q
L S F N D Y A B W
O C U F G P S P I
S G Z N O Z B Y F
S H R A C D D E P
O J W V Q E I R E
M T H D S W R L N
S Y D B G R A S S
H G Z I G R G Q U
S R B O O T S H A
Y L F R E T T U B
```

BLOSSOMS   **BUTTERFLY**   **GARDEN**
BOOTS   **DAFFODILS**   **GRASS**

Can you find the two umbrellas that match?

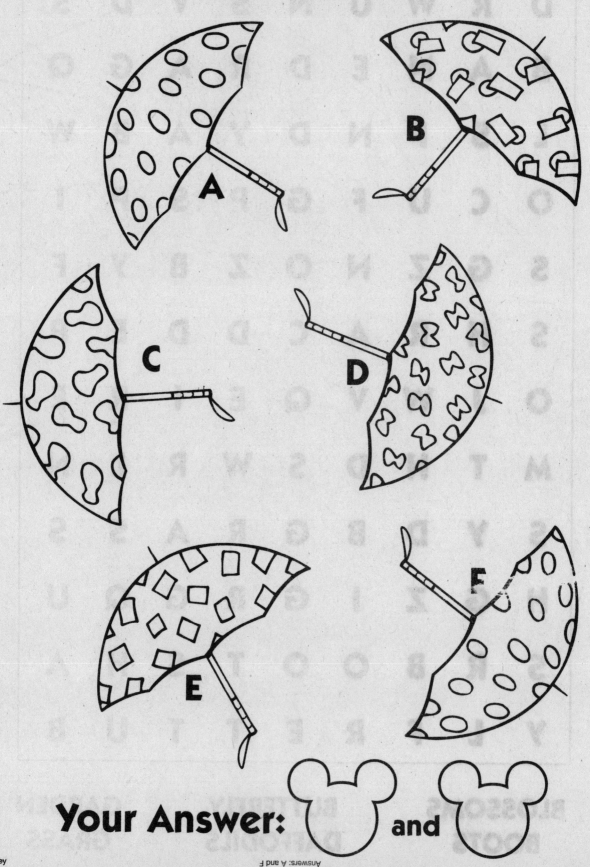

A B C D E F

Your Answer: and

Mickey glides with the eagles.

A flamingo teaches Daisy how to stand.

Missed!

Who's in there?

© Disney

Monkey see, monkey do.

Pluto meets a mountain goat.

"Well, hello, big fella!"

A koala surprises Pluto.

"Now, what did I do with my hat?"

"Wheeee!"

"Here's how to track a lion..."

Minnie and Daisy take a pony ride.

How many words can you make from the letters in:

DAISY DUCK

_____

_____

_____

_____

_____

_____

_____

Which Goofy is different?

A

B

C

D

Your Answer:

"Thanks for the umbrella!"

The perfect picture takes teamwork.

© Disney

Juggle and giggle!

"Scram!"

"Great shot!"

"We're outta here!"